JANE SAVES THE CANYON

WeActivism™, Volume 1

SAVE THE CANYON

By Shawne V. Shiflett
Illustrations by Blueberry Illustrations

JANE saves the CANYON

WeActivism™, Volume 1

Shawne V. Shiflett
Author

Blueberry Illustrations
Illustrator

Leigh Moore
Editor

This book is dedicated to

the people who only see possibilities
and through their action prompt us to rise
to the occasion and become our best selves.

what is WeActivism™?

WeActivism™ is what can happen when we all work together to achieve a common goal. This series seeks to shine a light on the individuals who IGNITE and INSPIRE such action as well as encourage its readers to get involved in the big issues they face in their own communities.

WeActivism™ is the type of action

Which occurs like a chemical reaction

When one of us comes to the conclusion

That it takes all of us to find the solution

The process starts inside the ME

Who identifies the problems that be

And educates us all to see

The power of harnessing the WE

Jane went for a hike
one crisp afternoon,

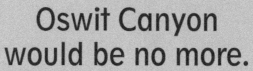

Oswit Canyon
would be no more.

Developers had something
else in store.

How could this be
the Canyon's fate?

Without a
smidgen of
concern over
the "how",

Our Jane was determined to stop the plow!

DECEMBER 2019
Sun Mon Tue Wed Thu Fri Sat
01 02 03 04 05 06 07
08 09 10 11 12 13 14
15 16 17 18 19 20 21
22 23 24 25 26 27 28
29 30 31 01 02 03 04
MAY 14 2019
But the deadline to comply was much too soon!

And just like the Lorax
who spoke for the trees,
Jane's voice was carried
by a midsummer's breeze.

ON DECEMBER 12, 2019 Jane and friends reached their GOAL and successfully SAVED THE CANYON!

On October 30, 2020 Oswit Land Trust officially BOUGHT THE CANYON!

"It was a long hard battle to save Oswit Canyon, but it was well worth the effort! Not only did we save this spectacular canyon for all the wildlife who call it home but we proved you can accomplish anything you set your mind to despite the obstacles that seemingly stand in your way. This book is the story of never giving up on something you believe in. You can follow your heart and make a difference in this world!"

Jane Garrison

HOW TO DONATE

Additional funds will be needed to cover ongoing expenses including:

- Property taxes (Oswit Land Trust will hold the title for the land.)
- Maintenance fees for property
- Insurance
- Potential additional property purchases

DONATE AT

www.oswitlandtrust.org

Jane Garrison

Prior to fighting for Oswit Canyon, Jane built two successful companies with her husband, one of which holds the patent on a product for kidney failure in dogs and cats and is distributed in 14 countries. Although new to land protection, Jane has been an advocate for animals for 25 years. In fact, she is often a guest on CNN as their Animal Specialist. One of her highlights over the years was heading up the animal rescue effort in New Orleans following Hurricane Katrina. Her work for this effort was the focus of two specials on Animal Planet and a special on National Geographic. She was also one of 10 people featured in a book titled "The Heroes of Hurricane Katrina". Jane worked for many years as an Elephant Specialist. During that time, she lived in Africa, spent time in Thailand and worked for the protection of elephants all over the world. She contributed to a book published by Smithsonian regarding ethics and elephants. Jane shares her home with her husband and their rescued dog and kitty.
This is not the first time Jane has inspired WeActivism™.
For her, it is a way of life.

THE 4A FORMULA

A note from the author: Jane Saves the Canyon is a poem about a real-life extraordinary effort. Jane happens to be my cousin by marriage. Her husband Mark and I share the same great grandparents. Dr. Mark is extraordinary on his own! I wrote the poem as a thank you for their hospitality while visiting them in California. I was fortunate enough to see Jane in action at an in-home gathering where Jane laid out what was at stake in the fight to save Oswit. Clearly, I was moved. I believe there is a formula for WeActivism™ represented by Jane's effort to save the canyon. I believe this type of energy can be duplicated! The question is, do you?

The 4A FORMULA:

Acknowledge the problem. State it clearly.

Accept all unbiased information about the issue/problem and the obstacles. Educate yourself!

Act and take steps necessary to overcome the foreseen obstacles.

Access the power of WE! Engage, ignite and inspire others to assist in your cause based on the information you have gathered and the way forward you are paving with the actions you are taking.

Save Oswit Canyon's 4A FORMULA

Acknowledge the problem.
Why did the Canyon need to be saved?
A developer wanted to build houses on 114 acres in Oswit Canyon which would have a negative impact as detailed below.

Accept all unbiased information about the issue/problem and the obstacles.

Impacts of the build:
- The South Lykken Trail and Oswit Canyon are prime internationally known ecotourist destinations in Palm Springs that draw thousands annually. Development here would remove them forever.
- This area is home to endangered Peninsular Bighorn Sheep and other flora and fauna unique to this area.
- Development of this alluvial fan would result in the building of a massive ¼-mile long retention dam at the back of the development. It would permanently scar the land and be viewable by tens of thousands, including the owners of any homes in that development. It would be impossible to hide a structure that long and at that elevation.
- Decreased home values both during and after construction, which would last up to ten years.
- This suburban housing development plan is totally unlike anything ever built in Palm Springs.
- Increased noise and dust.
- Potential for another partially built failed development after the destruction of the canyon.
- Increased light pollution.

Act.

- Created a Non-Profit: Save Oswit Canyon, Inc. is a non-profit 501(c)(3) organization (EIN 83-2006672) that exists solely to save the canyon. Save Oswit Canyon, Inc. is a local all-volunteer organization led by Jane Garrison.
- Since organizing in 2016: The organization collected over 5,000 signatures for an initiative to rezone the property from dense housing to environmentally sensitive, lobbied city officials, held rallies and meetings, filed litigation against the developer, and educated the public. It became clear that the only way to prevent this land from being developed was to purchase it as open space for future generations.

Access the power of WE!

- An $8,600,000 settlement was reached after a four-year battle. The group would have to raise this much money to purchase the property from the property owners, or the development would go forward.
- A deadline of December 31, 2019 to raise this money was set as a result of mediation among the City of Palm Springs, the property owners and Save Oswit Canyon, Inc. in May 2019.
- Jane found available grant money for $6,600,000 from both state and federal programs and secured a $1,000,000 contribution from the City of Palm Springs.
- Jane and her non-profit raised the remaining $1,000,000 needed from the public from July to December 31, 2019 to stop the construction plan. These funds were raised through holding many house parties in neighborhoods throughout Palm Springs.

Ideas to help start a WEActivism™ project in your neck of the woods

MAKE A LIST

- Write down a list of challenges in your school, neighborhood or community you believe the 4A Formula could resolve.

REREAD YOUR LIST

- Which challenges would others help you with?
- Which challenges feel possible to resolve?
- Which challenge are you the most excited about?
- Pick your first project!

NOW APPLY THE 4A FORMULA

Send us your 4A FORMULA story at info@weactivism.com.

VOCABULARY

activism - the doctrine or practice of vigorous action or involvement as a means of achieving goals.

investigate - to look into carefully and closely so as to learn the facts; examine.

fate - what happens to a person or thing in the end.

smidgen – a very small amount; bit.

sprawl - to spread in a manner that is not ordered or organized.

settlement - an agreement.

lobby - to try to get legislators to vote in a certain way.

rally - to call together for some common goal; assemble.

donation - the act or an instance of giving.

alluvial fan - a triangle-shaped deposit of gravel, sand, and even smaller pieces of sediment, such as silt (called alluvium) usually created as flowing water interacts with mountains, hills, or the steep walls of canyons.

endangered species - a species of plant or animal that is in danger of becoming extinct (no longer existing).

The Lorax - The Lorax is a children's book written by Dr. Seuss and first published in 1971. It chronicles the plight of the environment. The Lorax is the main character who "speaks for the trees" and confronts the Once-ler, who causes environmental destruction.

All facts and information about this effort in this book were obtained from Save Oswit Canyon's website, www.saveoswitcanyon.org and the organization's Facebook page, Save Oswit Canyon and Lykken Hiking Trail. Definitions on the vocabulary page were obtained from www.kids.wordsmyth.net, www.nationalgeorgraphic.org (Alluvial Fan), and Wikipedia (The Lorax) with minor editing for clarity.

CPSIA information can be obtained
at www.ICGtesting.com
Printed in the USA
LVHW072124211220
674623LV00026B/43

9 780578 665634